THIS JOURNAL BELONGS TO:

....

CONTACT INFO:

....

PASSPORT NUMBER:

....

D0961964

KIDS'
TRAVEL
JOURNAL

PETER PAUPER PRESS, INC.
WHITE PLAINS, NEW YORK

PETER PAUPER PRESS
Fine Books and Gifts Since 1928

In 1928, at the age of twenty-two, Peter Beilenson began printing books on a small press in the basement of his parents' home in Larchmont, New York. Peter—and later, his wife, Edna—sought to create fine books that sold at "prices even a pauper could afford."

Today, still family owned and operated, Peter Pauper Press continues to honor our founders' legacy of quality, value, and fun for big kids and small kids alike.

Designed by Heather Zschock

Copyright © 2015
Peter Pauper Press, Inc.
202 Mamaroneck Avenue
White Plains, NY 10601
ISBN 978-1-4413-1814-5
Printed in China
7

Visit us at www.peterpauper.com

CONTENTS

LET'S GET GOING!

Taking a trip?
Going on vacation?

Great!

Use this journal to keep a record of everything! Plan your packing list, write down what you did, sketch what you see, rate each day, paste in photos, tickets, maps, postcards, and more. You can keep more stuff in the back pocket. There are maps of the world, North America, and Europe, plus helpful words and phrases in other languages, world facts, puzzles, games, and more. Let's go!

A little magic can take you a long way.

—ROALD DAHL, *JAMES AND THE GIANT PEACH*

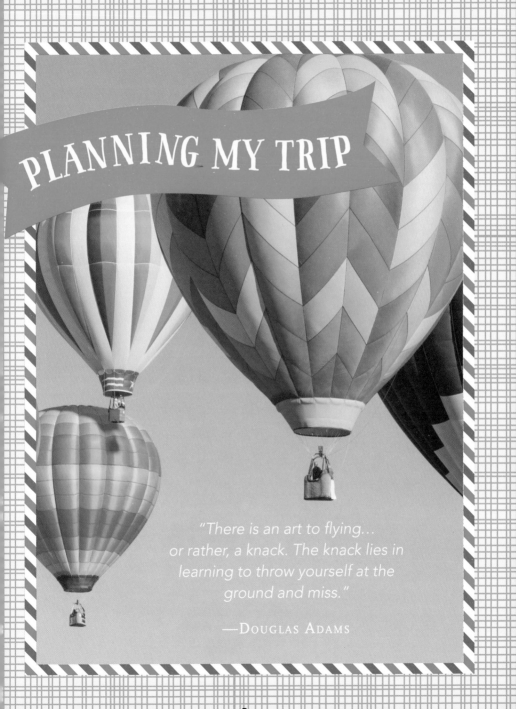

PLANNING MY TRIP

"There is an art to flying...
or rather, a knack. The knack lies in
learning to throw yourself at the
ground and miss."

—Douglas Adams

Place

Language

Time zone

Currency

Anthem (the national song)

Flag (draw a picture here)

Landmarks

More facts

WHEN WE'RE GOING

What's the plan, Stan? Are you hitting the road in a week or next summer? How long will you be gone?

WHO'S GOING

Family and/or friends? Thoughts about how folks might get along with each other? Who do you want to hang with the most? Any meet-ups planned?

WHAT I'D LIKE TO SEE AND DO

Go wild or relax? Explore and hike, or lounge and read? Include sights and shows to see, places to eat, landmarks, museums, parks, and shops. Do a little research ahead of time to learn about stuff for your wish list.

"Second star to the right, and straight on till morning."
That, Peter had told Wendy, was the way to the Neverland.

—J. M. BARRIE, _PETER PAN_

ITINERARY

TICKET

Day 1

Day 2

Day 3 The trees are Plowing
Prity fast.

Day 4

Day 5

Day 6

Day 7

Day 8

Day 9

Day 10

Day 11

Day 12

_____

_____

_____

_____

Day 13

_____

_____

_____

_____

Day 14

_____

_____

_____

_____

*May the wind under your wings bear you where
the sun sails and the moon walks.*

— J. R. R. TOLKIEN, *THE HOBBIT*

IMPORTANT CONTACTS

Name

Address

Phone

Email

Name

Address

Phone

Email

Name

Address

Phone

Email

Name

Address

Phone

Email

Name

Address

Phone

Email

Name

Address

Phone

Email

Name

Address

Phone

Email

Name

Address

Phone

Email

**Will someone need to make an international call?
You can look up country calling codes at
www.countrycallingcodes.com**

MY PACKING LIST

Check off items as you pack them.

CLOTHES

- [ ] Sleepwear
- [ ] Underwear
- [ ] Socks
- [ ] Pants
- [ ] Shorts
- [ ] Long-sleeved tops
- [ ] T-shirts
- [ ] Dressy clothes
- [ ] Jackets
- [ ] Bathing suit
- [ ] Winter accessories
- [ ] Hats
- [ ] Belts
- [ ] _____
- [ ] _____
- [ ] _____
- [ ] _____

FOOTWEAR

- [ ] Everyday shoes
- [ ] Sneakers
- [ ] Slippers
- [ ] Sandals
- [ ] Flip-flops
- [ ] Dressy shoes
- [ ] Boots
- [ ] _____
- [ ] _____
- [ ] _____

PERSONAL ITEMS

- [ ] Soap
- [ ] Hair products
- [ ] Hair accessories
- [ ] Brush & comb
- [ ] Blow dryer

- [ ] Toothbrush & toothpaste
- [ ] Floss & mouthwash
- [ ] Moisturizer
- [ ] Eyecare products
- [ ] Nail file, tweezers, scissors
- [ ] Vitamins & medicine
- [ ] ....
- [ ] ....
- [ ] ....

THINGS FOR THE TRIP

- [ ] Passport
- [ ] Itinerary & tickets
- [ ] Drinks & snacks
- [ ] Cell phone & charger
- [ ] Money
- [ ] Reading material
- [ ] Audio books
- [ ] Music
- [ ] Sunglasses

- [ ] Camera and charger
- [ ] Games
- [ ] ....
- [ ] ....
- [ ] ....

MISCELLANEOUS

- [ ] Tissues
- [ ] Batteries
- [ ] Flashlight
- [ ] Umbrella
- [ ] Jewelry & watches
- [ ] Laundry bag
- [ ] Binoculars
- [ ] Bug spray
- [ ] Sunscreen
- [ ] Exercise gear
- [ ] ....
- [ ] ....
- [ ] ....

Don't forget to bring this Travel Journal and your pencils, pens, and/or art supplies to write and draw in it!

TIME TO GO!

It is good to have an end to journey towards; but
it is the journey that matters, in the end.

—URSULA K. LE GUIN

HOW WE'RE GETTING THERE

○ **By plane?** ○ **By train?** ○ **By ship?**   ○ **By bus?**
○ **By auto?**   ○ **By taxi?**   ○ **By bicycle?** ○ **Other**

Write the details or draw them here:

Fasten your safety belts, clench your buttocks!
It's going to be a bumpy ride!

—SHRUNKEN HEAD, *HARRY POTTER AND THE PRISONER OF AZKABAN* FILM

WHEN DO WE LEAVE?

WHAT HAPPENED ON THE WAY?

Sometimes the journey is as awesome as the destination.

WE'RE THERE!

Stuff your eyes with wonder....
See the world.

—RAY BRADBURY, *FAHRENHEIT 451*

WHAT I SAW FIRST

Write the details or draw them here.

WHERE WE STAYED

Swanky hotel or a relative's house? Bed and breakfast or campsite? What did you like, and what not so much? Was it comfy? In the city or the country?

HOW WE GOT AROUND

You have brains in your head.
You have feet in your shoes.
You can steer yourself
any direction you choose.

—DR. SEUSS, OH, THE PLACES YOU'LL GO!

WHO WE MET

People-watching in new places is fascinating. Strangers you meet on vacation—
from tour guides to waiters to taxi drivers—can give inside info on where you are.

*Travelers never think
that they are the
foreigners.*

—MASON COOLEY

TAKING IT IN

Write the details or draw them here:

Sounds

Smells

Weather

WHAT WE SAW

AND DID

The whole world is full of things, and somebody has to look for them.

—ASTRID LINDGREN,
PIPPI LONGSTOCKING

DAILY JOURNAL

Date

Location

What we did

HOW WAS YOUR DAY?

○ Fun ○ Amazing ○ Fine ○ Boring
○ Crazy ○ Exhausting ○

RATE IT!

☆☆☆☆☆

YOUR MOOD:

☺ ☺ ☺ ☹

DAILY JOURNAL

Date

Location

What we did

HOW WAS YOUR DAY?

○ Fun ○ Amazing ○ Fine ○ Boring

○ Crazy ○ Exhausting ○ _____

RATE IT!

☆ ☆ ☆ ☆ ☆

YOUR MOOD:

☺ ☺ ☺ ☹

DAILY JOURNAL

Date

Location

What we did

HOW WAS YOUR DAY?

○ Fun   ○ Amazing   ○ Fine   ○ Boring

○ Crazy   ○ Exhausting   ○ _____

RATE IT!

☆ ☆ ☆ ☆ ☆

YOUR MOOD:

😀   🙂   😐   ☹️

DAILY JOURNAL

Date

Location

What we did

HOW WAS YOUR DAY?

○ Fun   ○ Amazing   ○ Fine   ○ Boring

○ Crazy   ○ Exhausting   ○

RATE IT!

☆☆☆☆☆

YOUR MOOD:

😃   🙂   😐   🙁

DAILY JOURNAL

Date

Location

What we did

HOW WAS YOUR DAY?

○ Fun   ○ Amazing   ○ Fine   ○ Boring

○ Crazy   ○ Exhausting   ○

RATE IT!

☆ ☆ ☆ ☆ ☆

YOUR MOOD:

☺ ☺ ☺ ☹

DAILY JOURNAL

Date

Location

What we did

HOW WAS YOUR DAY?

○ Fun   ○ Amazing   ○ Fine   ○ Boring

○ Crazy   ○ Exhausting   ○ _____

RATE IT!

☆ ☆ ☆ ☆ ☆

YOUR MOOD:

😃   🙂   😐   ☹️

DAILY JOURNAL

Date

Location

What we did

HOW WAS YOUR DAY?

○ Fun   ○ Amazing   ○ Fine   ○ Boring

○ Crazy   ○ Exhausting   ○

RATE IT!

☆ ☆ ☆ ☆ ☆

YOUR MOOD:

☺   ☺   😐   ☹

DAILY JOURNAL

Date

Location

What we did

HOW WAS YOUR DAY?

○ Fun   ○ Amazing   ○ Fine   ○ Boring

○ Crazy   ○ Exhausting   ○

RATE IT!

☆☆☆☆☆

YOUR MOOD:

😀   🙂   😐   🙁

DAILY JOURNAL

Date

Location

What we did

HOW WAS YOUR DAY?

○ Fun   ○ Amazing   ○ Fine   ○ Boring

○ Crazy   ○ Exhausting   ○

RATE IT!

☆ ☆ ☆ ☆ ☆

YOUR MOOD:

😀   🙂   😐   🙁

DAILY JOURNAL

Date

Location

What we did

HOW WAS YOUR DAY?

○ Fun ○ Amazing ○ Fine ○ Boring

○ Crazy ○ Exhausting ○

RATE IT!

☆☆☆☆☆

YOUR MOOD:

☺ ☺ ☺ ☹

DAILY JOURNAL

Date

Location

What we did

HOW WAS YOUR DAY?

- ○ Fun
- ○ Amazing
- ○ Fine
- ○ Boring
- ○ Crazy
- ○ Exhausting
- ○

RATE IT!

☆ ☆ ☆ ☆ ☆

YOUR MOOD:

😃 ☺ 😐 ☹

DAILY JOURNAL

Date

Location

What we did

HOW WAS YOUR DAY?

○ Fun   ○ Amazing   ○ Fine   ○ Boring

○ Crazy   ○ Exhausting   ○

RATE IT!	YOUR MOOD:
☆ ☆ ☆ ☆ ☆	😀 🙂 😐 🙁

DAILY JOURNAL

Date

Location

What we did

HOW WAS YOUR DAY?

○ Fun   ○ Amazing   ○ Fine   ○ Boring

○ Crazy   ○ Exhausting   ○

RATE IT!

☆☆☆☆☆

YOUR MOOD:

😀   🙂   😐   ☹️

DAILY JOURNAL

Date

Location

What we did

HOW WAS YOUR DAY?

O Fun   O Amazing   O Fine   O Boring

O Crazy   O Exhausting   O

RATE IT!

☆☆☆☆☆

YOUR MOOD:

😀   🙂   😐   ☹️

DAILY JOURNAL

Date

Location

What we did

HOW WAS YOUR DAY?

○ Fun   ○ Amazing   ○ Fine   ○ Boring

○ Crazy   ○ Exhausting   ○

RATE IT!

☆ ☆ ☆ ☆ ☆

YOUR MOOD:

😃   🙂   😐   ☹️

Write or draw what you saw and what you bought.
Take note of cool displays or shops.

FOOD

Write or draw what you tasted or ate—and any foods you eschewed
(as opposed to "chewed"). Include fun restaurants, food trucks,
and grocery stores. How are they different from at home?

THAT'S AMAZING!

What were the top ten amazing things you saw or did? Write them in the stars!

WEIRDEST THINGS WE DID

GAMES AND PUZZLES

The worst thing about being a tourist is having other tourists recognize you as a tourist.

—RUSSELL BAKER

SO LONG, FAREWELL . . .

How do you say goodbye? Find these farewell words hidden backward and forward, horizontally, vertically, and diagonally in the word search below.

```
O  L  L  E  W  E  R  A  F  S  P
E  R  S  C  R  S  E  E  Y  A  O
T  A  K  E  I  T  E  A  S  Y  T
M  E  T  M  L  A  D  B  D  E  A
I  A  U  T  S  I  O  J  K  E  K
L  D  O  G  O  T  T  O  G  S  E
Z  I  I  S  L  O  G  I  P  B  C
V  E  X  H  O  D  E  K  Q  R  A
S  U  N  W  N  P  F  Y  U  I  R
C  N  O  M  G  O  O  D  B  Y  E
P  A  U  R  E  V  O  I  R  L  K
```

- adieu
- adios
- au revoir
- bye
- ciao
- farewell
- goodbye
- got to go
- later
- see ya
- so long
- take care
- take it easy

51

Take turns connecting two dots. If you complete a square, write your initial inside. Whoever has the most boxes at the end of the game wins!

ROAD RULES

Stop! There's only One Way to read the words below. Unscramble the roadside signs on the left and write the correct words on the right. Then put the circled letters in the blanks below in order to answer the riddle.

AWKL NOTD __ __ __ __   __ __ __ __

XTIE __ __ __ __

SEDOLC __ __ __ __ __ __

SUB PSOT __ __ __   __ __ __ __

DLIYE __ __ __ __ __

PEON __ __ __ __

PHELETONE __ __ __ __ __ __ __ __ __

ALKW __ __ __ __

GERNAD __ __ __ __ __ __

NOE YAW __ __ __ __ __ __

WHERE CAN YOU ALWAYS FIND GAS?

IN THE __ __ __ __ __ __ __ __ __

IT ALL ADDS UP

Fill in the numbers 1-9 in the boxes so that the sum of any three numbers going up down, across, or diagonally equals 15.

BIRTHDAY CROSSWORD

ACROSS

1. Happy _____!
7. Opposite of off
9. Gobbled
10. Either __
11. America Online: abbr.
12. Crepe paper decorations
14. Lighted
15. Pester
16. "___ phone home"
18. What 8-Down does
22. "How ___ are you now?"
24. ____ and ahhs
25. Countdown number
27. Tricky tactic
29. Wise one
32. Blow out your candles and make a _____
35. Belonging to you
37. Soaked
38. Anagram of 34-Down

DOWN

1. Decorations full of hot air
2. Party game exclamation, "You're __!"
3. What your parents need after your party
4. You toot them
5. "You made my _____ come true."
6. "Delicious!"
7. Rowboat pole
8. Schnozz
13. What birthdays measure
17. __ and fro
19. Laughing out loud: abbr.
20. Crazy
21. Timid
23. Poodle, for one
26. Original
28. Birthdays celebrate the day you were _____
30. High card
31. Old __ the hills
33. He, she, or ___
34. Santa saying, when repeated three times
36. Orange juice: abbr.

HIDDEN ISLANDS

Find the names of these islands in the word search below. They're hidden backward and forward, horizontally, vertically, and diagonally.

```
B  P  I  T  I  H  A  T  L  I  N  H
S  I  C  I  L  Y  E  I  J  D  M  O
G  R  E  A  T  B  R  I  T  A  I  N
J  Z  L  A  R  P  F  C  P  B  J  G
A  V  A  I  A  U  Y  F  O  U  K  K
P  O  N  C  G  H  B  Q  U  C  R  O
A  X  D  I  I  A  W  A  H  L  S  N
N  U  W  T  B  E  R  M  U  D  A  G
```

- Aruba
- Bermuda
- Capri
- Cuba
- Fiji
- Great Britain
- Hawaii
- Hong Kong
- Iceland
- Japan
- Sicily
- Tahiti

ABC HUNT

Look around as you're traveling. See if you can find something that begins with each letter of the alphabet. You may have to get creative with some of the letters!

A ....

B ....

C ....

D ....

E ....

F ....

G ....

H ....

I ....

J ....

K ....

L ....

M ....

N ....

O ....

P ....

Q ....

R ....

S ....

T ....

U ....

V ....

W ....

X ....

Y ....

Z ....

WHAT COUNTS?

Count the things around you. Can you find things to put in each numbered circle? For example, you might see 1 police officer, 2 taxis, 3 pigeons, etc.

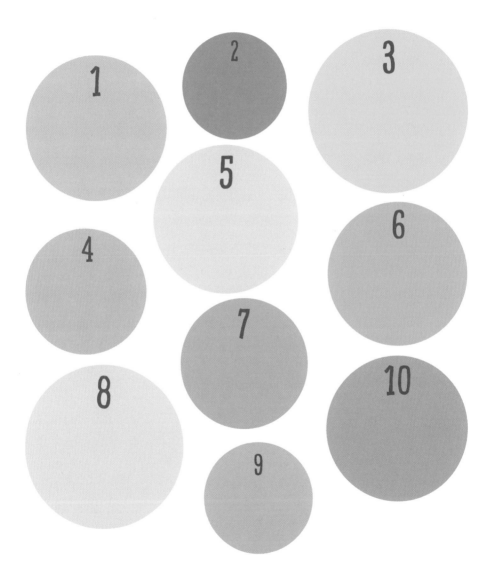

CATEGORIES

Pick a letter and a category below. Players take turns naming something in the category that starts with that letter. For example, if you chose the letter B and Food, players might say: bread, banana, blueberries, etc. Last player to name a correct word chooses the next letter and category. Check off the games you've played in the grid below.

CATEGORIES	B	T	M	H	S
Animals					
Food					
Autos					
Cities					
Movie stars					
TV shows					
Girls' names					
Boys' names					
Songs					
Things at hardware store					
Things at a sports stadium					
Things in your closet					

TWENTY QUESTIONS A game for two or more players

Think of something—anything you like. Other players take turns asking yes-or-no questions to figure out what it is. For example, one person might ask, "Is it alive?" The next person might ask, "Is it an animal?" The first person to guess correctly before the 20 questions are up wins.

BORED? Bubble gum required

Have a bubble gum blowing contest! The person to blow the biggest bubble wins! What's your favorite flavor? Which kind makes the biggest bubbles?

IF YOU'RE REALLY BORED...

Count stuff! Count anything you see: restaurants, colored mailboxes, yellow cars, red houses...

MORE MEMORIES

Write or draw more memories and impressions on these pages!

BEEN THERE. DONE THAT. GOT THE T-SHIRT.

Draw your favorite souvenir T-shirt from your trip. Put a photo of you wearing it on the next page.

TA DA!

Paste a photo of you wearing your T-shirt here.

LET'S TALK!

What new words or expressions did you learn? Write them here.

FAVORITE PHOTOS

THE TRIP HOME

The real voyage of
discovery consists not in
seeking new landscapes,
but in having new eyes.
—MARCEL PROUST

HOW WE'RE GETTING BACK

○ By plane? ○ By train? ○ By ship? ○ By bus?
○ By auto? ○ By taxi? ○ By bicycle? ○ Other

When do we leave?

Write the details or draw them here:

WHAT HAPPENED ON THE WAY HOME?

Smooth sailing or mishaps? Any unexpected detours, delays, or added adventure?

FREE WRITING

Here's your place to write or draw more vacation impressions. What was fun and what disappointed? Did you learn anything—maybe about yourself? Are there places you want to revisit? People to stay in touch with? Tape and glue stuff down on these pages, too, if you want.

*I've always liked the idea that
writing is a form of travel.*

—RICK RIORDAN

SOUVENIRS

SOUVENIRS

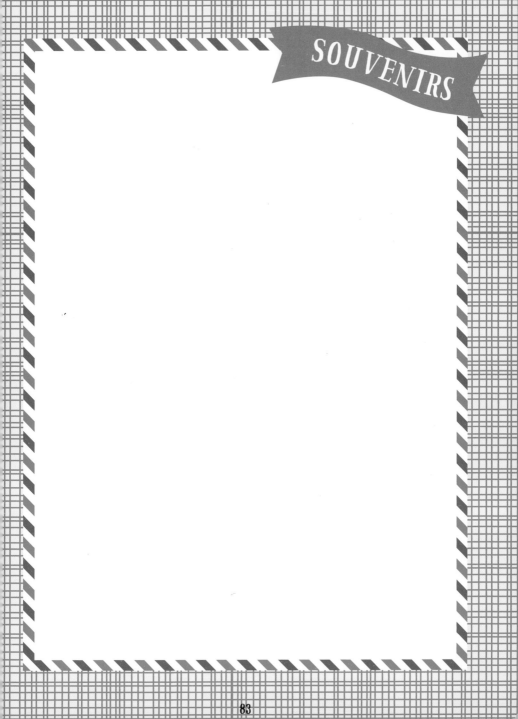

SOUVENIRS

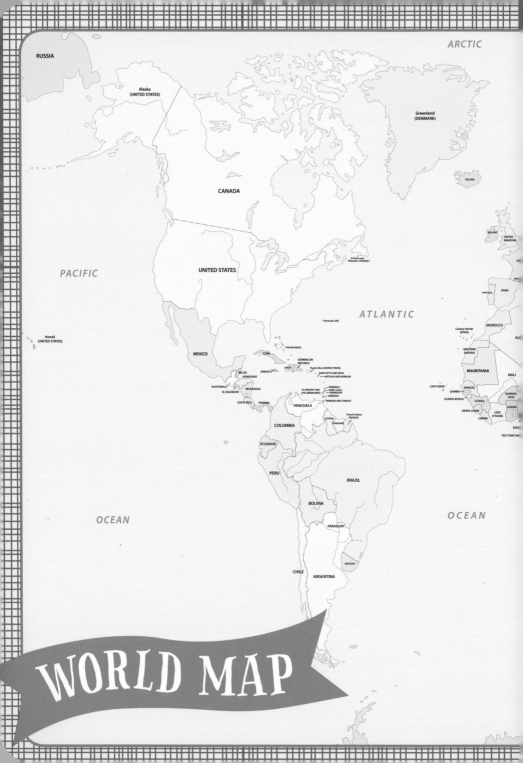

WORLD MAP

NORTH AMERICA MAP

I often don't know where my luggage is, that's what being a tourist is all about.

—Terry Pratchett, *The Light Fantastic*

RUSSIA

*Bering
Sea*

Gul
Alas

PACIFIC

OCEAN

Hawaii

PACIFIC

OCEAN

FOREIGN WORDS AND PHRASES

ENGLISH	FRENCH	SOUNDS LIKE
Hello	*Bonjour*	*(bohn-zhoor)*
Good evening	*Bon soir*	*(bohn swah)*
Please	*S'il vous plaît*	*(sill voo pleh)*
Where is the bathroom?	*Où sont les toilettes?*	*(Ooo son lays twah-lehts?)*
I'm sorry, I don't speak French	*Je suis désolé, je ne parle pas Français*	*(zhuh swee day-zoh-lay, zhuh nuh parl pah frahn-say)*
How much does that cost?	*Ça coûte combien?*	*(Sah koot kombee-en?)*
Thank you	*Merci*	*(mare-see)*
Good-bye	*Au revoir*	*(oh-vwar)*

ENGLISH	SPANISH	SOUNDS LIKE
Hello	*Hola*	*(oh-lah)*
Please	*Por favor*	*(por-fa-bor)*
Where is the bathroom?	*¿Dónde están los servicios?*	*(dohn-day ay-stahn lohs sehr-bee-thee-ohs)*
I'm sorry, I don't speak Spanish	*Lo siento, no hablo español*	*(loh-see-ehn-toh no ah-bloh ay-spahn-yohl)*
How much does that cost?	*¿Cuánto cuesta?*	*(kwahn-toh kway-stah)*
Thank you	*Gracias*	*(grah-thee-ahs)*
Good-bye	*Adios*	*(ah-dee-ohs)*

ENGLISH	ITALIAN	SOUNDS LIKE
Good morning	*Buon giorno*	(boo-ohn jeeor-no)
Good afternoon/ evening	*Buona sera*	(boo-ohna sehr-ah)
Good night	*Buona notte*	(boo-ohna noh-tay)
Please	*Per favore*	(pair fah-voh-reh)
Where is the bathroom?	*Dov'è il bagno?*	(Doh-veh eel baa-nii-ooh)
I'm sorry, I don't speak Italian	*Mi dispiace, non parlo italiano*	(mee dees-pya-che, non par-lo ay-tal-lee-on-o)
How much is this?	*Quanto costa?*	(kwan-toh cost-ah)
Thank you	*Grazie*	(grah-tsee-yay)
Hi/Bye	*Ciao*	(chow)
Good-bye	*Arrivederci*	(ah-ree-veh-dehr-chee)

PRACTICAL STUFF

METRICS

Distance
1 inch (in) = 2.54 centimeters (cm)
1 yard (yd) = 0.91 meters (m)
3.28 feet (ft) = 1 meter (m)
1 mile (mi) = 1.61 kilometers (km)
0.62 mile (mi) = 1 kilometer (km)

Volume
1 ounce (oz) = 29.57 milliliters (ml)
8 ounces (oz) = 236.59 milliliters (ml)
33.81 fluid ounces (oz) or .26 gallons = 1 liter

Weight
1 ounce (oz) = 28.35 grams (g)
1 pound = 0.45 kilograms (kg)
2.20 pounds = 1 kilogram (kg)

Area
1 hectare = 10,000 m² = 2.47 acres

Temperature

32 degrees Fahrenheit (°F) = 0 degrees Celsius (°C)
50 degrees Fahrenheit (°F) = 10 degrees Celsius (°C)
68 degrees Fahrenheit (°F) = 20 degrees Celsius (°C)
86 degrees Fahrenheit (°F) = 30 degrees Celsius (°C)

Here is a helpful poem to remember in countries
that use Celsius temperatures:

30 is hot,
20 is nice,
10 put a coat on,
and 0 is ice.

MONEY MATTERS

Pound It Out

Going to London or other parts of the United Kingdom (U.K.)
of Britain? Britain's currency is the pound sterling (£). One pound
or £1 equals 100p, or pence. A "quid" refers to a pound,
and pence are often just called "p."

Euro-sense

Traveling to France, Spain, or Italy, or other countries in
the European Union? Prices are written this way: Twenty euros
and fifty euro cents (centesimi) = €20,50. Two thousand
euros and fifty euro cents = €2.000,50

France is the most visited country in the world, with more than 80 million visitors per year. Its Louvre Museum, in Paris, home of the famous Mona Lisa painting by Leonardo da Vinci, is the most visited art museum on the planet.

The Japanese name for the country of **Japan** is *Nippon* or *Nihon*, which means "Land of the Rising Sun" or "Sun Origin."

Canada is the second largest country in the world by total area after Russia, and it has the longest coastline in the world.

The London Underground subway system, or Tube, was the first of its kind in the world and opened in 1863. **London** is also home to one of the largest Ferris wheels in the world: the London Eye, which is 135 meters or about 443 feet tall.

To remember the names of the **Great Lakes**, think of the word HOMES: Huron, Ontario, Michigan, Erie, Superior.

Australia is the only country that is also an entire continent. It has more reptile species (over 917) than any other country, and is home to unique animals, such as the kookaburra, the platypus, and the wombat.

Alert, a settlement in the Canadian territory of Nunavut, is the northernmost permanently inhabited place in the world. It's located at a latitude of 82°30'N, or just 508 miles (817 kilometers) from the North Pole!

94

The longest single-word place name in the world is *Taumatawhakatangi-hangakoauauotamateaturipukakapikimaungahoronukupokaiwhenuaki-tanatahu*, the name of a hill in **New Zealand**. It's a Maori (native New Zealander) word that means "the place where Tamatea, the man with the big knees, who slid, climbed, and swallowed mountains, known as 'land-eater,' played his flute to his loved one."

While English is the official language of the whole UK, **Wales** also has a second official language of its own called Welsh. The two languages are treated as equals in that country, which is why signs there are written in both Welsh and English. *Iechyd da*! Cheers!

The country name **"Spain"** (in Spanish, *España*) may come from the ancient Punic word *I-Shpania*, which means "Land of rabbits." Spain is known for its relaxed lifestyle. The Spanish eat lunch from about 1:00 pm to 3:00 pm, and often don't eat dinner until at least 10:00 pm.

The Great Wall of China is the world's largest man-made structure. The most well-known parts, built during the Ming dynasty, stretch 5,500 miles or 8,850 kilometers! **China** has the largest population in the world, with over 1.3 billion people.

How long is the island of Manhattan, New York, U.S.A.?
Answer: About 13.4 miles.

The country of Egypt is home to one of the Seven Wonders of the Ancient World: the Great Pyramid of Giza.

Along a famous roadway network in Germany (or Deutschland in German) called the Autobahn, there is no mandated speed limit.

Madagascar, an island country off the coast of Africa, has a distinct ecology of its own and is sometimes called "the eighth continent." It is the only place in the world where lemurs, its small and adorable primates, are found.

The country of Brazil covers three time zones and is the only country in South America to use Portuguese as its national language. (This is because Portugal claimed the territory in 1500; Brazil became independent in 1822.)

What is the largest state in the United States? Alaska. It's 586,412 square miles! If you visit Alaska in the summer, don't forget your sunglasses! In summer, the sun stays out all day and practically all night.

The country of Italy looks like a giant boot extending into the Mediterranean Sea, about to kick the island of Sicily. The most popular sport in Italy is soccer (known as football in Europe), and the country has won four World Cups. Coincidence?